JIMMY THE LIZARD AND HIS GRAND ADVENTURE

BY AGYA KARKI PUDNER

JIMMY THE LIZARD AND HIS GRAND ADVENTURE
Text and images copyright © 2019 Agya Karki Pudner
ISBN: 978-0-9998969-2-1
Published by Mayuri Grace, LLC

*To all my students who inspire me
to remain a child at heart.*

*And to Jimmy, and my husband Steve,
for being the inspiration for this story.*

"Daddy, daddy what is
an adventure?"

"Hmmm ... adventure! I love that word. It makes me smile. I would say, an adventure is an exciting experience. I have had a lot of adventures in my life."

"Let me think ... oh, I have a good one!

This adventure is from a long time ago, when I lived in a little garden in front of a house.

I loved my rainbow garden. It had so many colorful fruits and vegetables growing all around me. But even more than the garden, I loved sitting by the big front window and watching the family that lived there."

"What I remember is that this family loved going for walks. They put their little boy in the stroller and went for a walk every day.

One day, I decided to join them. As they were getting ready, I quickly hopped in the stroller and hid inside it. Then the stroller started moving. Wow! It was like I was watching a movie."

"No wizards or ballerinas, but I saw houses, cars, dogs, and people. The cool breeze made me feel so free.

I got excited and wanted a better view, so I climbed higher and higher."

"But then, the dad saw me! I was so scared. I knew I was going to die! My entire life flashed before my eyes. I knew I had to think and act fast."

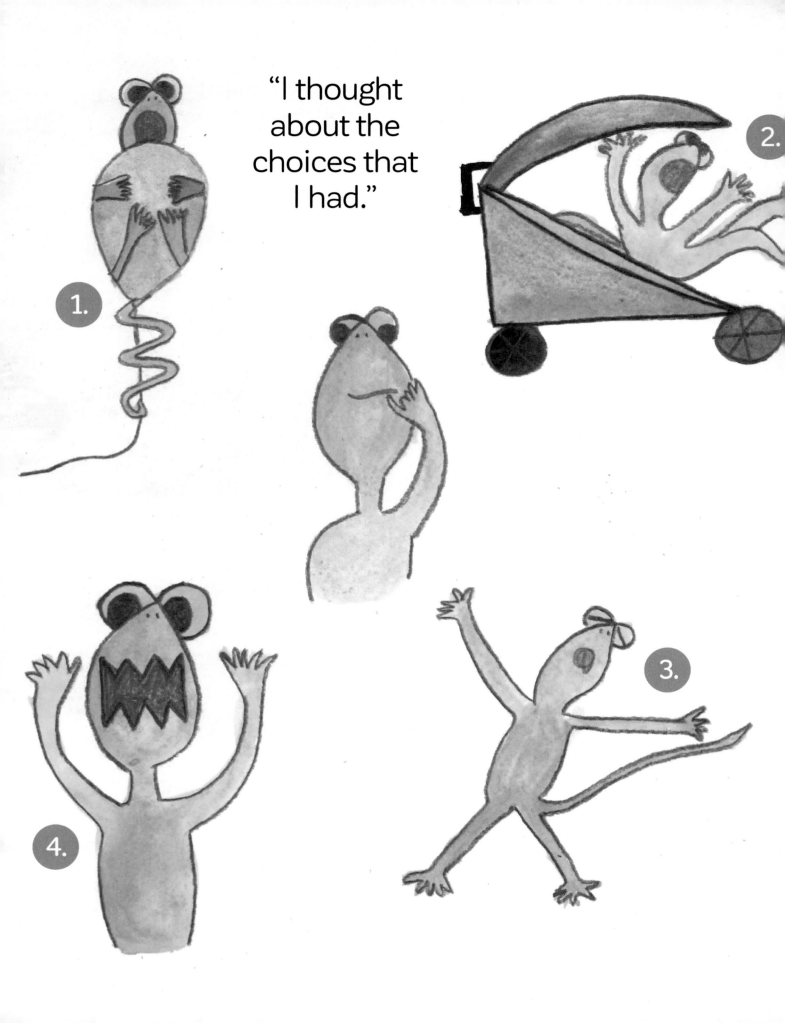

"I thought about the choices that I had."

1. "I could fly away in the boy's balloon ... but the balloon could pop!

2. I could jump out of the stroller ... but I could break my leg or hit my head!

3. I could play dead ... but what if the dad put me in a plastic bag and threw me in the trash can? Ewww!

4. I could make my mean scary face at them ... but no one had ever been scared of my super mean face until you guys came along."

"Then I thought about the choices the dad had.

1. He could get a branch and hit me.

2. He could shake the stroller and make me fall.

3. He could make me their family pet.

4. He could take me to court for trespassing."

The dad's choices ...

"I knew that I could not control what the dad would do.

I closed my eyes and thought back to my wonderful life and smiled. I chose to face death calmly.

I let the dad make the first move."

"Oh no daddy! What did the mean man do to you?"

"I still cannot believe what happened next.

The dad calmly and carefully took his baby out of the stroller and put him on his shoulders. The mommy did not even scream!

I think they were just as shocked as I was."

"Then I made the boldest choice of my life. Quick as lightning, I hopped in the front of the stroller and took the empty spot. That's when it happened ..."

"Even better, the mom started pushing me in the stroller! A squirrel saw me, who told the birds, who then told the butterflies. And before I knew it, I was known as the heroic stroller-riding lizard."

"Wow! Daddy!
You let someone
push you in a
stroller?"

"Daddy was a
baby! Daddy
was a baby!"

"Yes, she pushed me for the rest of the walk.

When we got home, I jumped out of the stroller and went back to my garden. All my friends were waiting to hear about my adventure."

"I had the
best dreams
that night!"

"The next morning, I was on the front page of our local newspaper!"

And that was the beginning of many more adventures to come."

LIZARD WORLD

Volume I

Mandolin star
page 7 ♫♫♫

RED NINJA CAFE

Page 12

Brothers open a cafe!

Sisters finish race hand in hand!

A BRAVE LIZARD'S HEROIC RIDE

LIFE IS A BEAUTIFUL RIDE

"Ooooh yes! There are many more adventures to tell you about, but let's save that for another time."

Everest Base Camp, Tibet

The Gobi desert
Mongolia

Teruel, Spain

Penguins!

Capetown, South Africa

Gulf shores, Alabama

Bhaktapur, Nepal

"You too will have a lot of adventures waiting for you in your life.

Just be open to new experiences and to meeting new people. Be prepared, don't be afraid to take risks, and remember to believe that good things will happen. And trust me, they will!"

AUTHOR'S NOTE: Jimmy was a real lizard who lived in my garden. Jimmy and I spent a lot of time watching each other through our big glass window. Jimmy really did come for a stroller ride with me and my family, and I had the privilege of pushing him around our neighborhood. Jimmy taught me to be open to new opportunities and excited about life. I have enjoyed writing this book and imagining the experience from Jimmy's perspective. I hope you enjoy reading this book, and I hope it inspires you to see your life as a beautiful adventure.

Agya Karki Pudner

Agya Karki Pudner grew up in Kathmandu, Nepal, moved to Virginia at the age of 18, and now lives in Homewood, Alabama. This is her second book. Her first book, The Magician Apple is a bilingual book created to promote her first language; Nepali. It is available for purchase through amazon.com. When not staring at lizards, she enjoys spending time with her husband and three children, playing the mandolin, and traveling.

Life is a beautiful ride!

Made in the USA
Middletown, DE
21 July 2020